TOWARDS BET

C000065026

TOWARDS BETHLEHEM

Stories & poems for Advent, Christmas & Epiphany

Janet Killeen

**wild goose
publications**

www.ionabooks.com

Copyright © Janet Killeen
Published 2020 by
Wild Goose Publications
21 Carlton Court, Glasgow G5 9JP, UK,
the publishing division of the Iona Community.
Scottish Charity No. SC003794. Limited Company Reg. No. SC096243.

ISBN 978-1-84952-751-4

Cover image © Pezibear from Pixabay

The publishers gratefully acknowledge the support of the Drummond Trust,
3 Pitt Terrace, Stirling FK8 2EY in producing this book.

All rights reserved. Apart from the circumstances described below relating to
non-commercial use, no part of this publication may be reproduced in any form or by
any means, including photocopying or any information storage or retrieval system,
without written permission from the publisher via PLSclear.com.

Non-commercial use:
The material in this book may be used *non-commercially* for worship and group work
without written permission from the publisher. If photocopies of small sections are
made, please make full acknowledgement of the source, and report usage to the CLA or
other copyright organisation.

Janet Killeen has asserted her right in accordance with the Copyright, Designs and
Patents Act, 1988, to be identified as the author of this work.

Overseas distribution
Australia: Willow Connection Pty Ltd, Unit 4A, 3–9 Kenneth Road,
Manly Vale, NSW 2093
New Zealand: Pleroma, Higginson Street, Otane 4170, Central Hawkes Bay

Printed by Bell & Bain, Thornliebank, Glasgow

CONTENTS

CONTENTS

INTRODUCTION

Working with the biblical narrative in Advent and over the Christmas season is a wonderful challenge. When I am imaginatively exploring these stories, I aim to use voices or perspectives that make the reader feel paradoxically unfamiliar with the story – 'what's going to happen next?'/'who is this?' – rather than, 'I know what's coming'. The familiarity of so much of the Christmas story might sometimes dull us to its shocking and uncomfortable elements. So many of the events and themes have parallels with our own day, so I've tried to keep a sense of contemporary relevance as well as take the reader back to what it might have felt like or been like at the time. My hope is that an image in a poem or story, or the breakthrough of a sense of smell or sight or touch may stir your imagination, so that, for a moment, you can hold both now and then together in an instant of time, and travel afresh towards Bethlehem.

Janet Killeen

ADVENT

GENEALOGY

Perhaps they met once. Imagine a shining day,
The sun rising in pearl and silver,
Before dust and heat press down
On travellers, stumbling their pace.

Where two roads join and flow together,
    Glimpsed across the backs of laden animals
    And the burdened shoulders of the crowd,
Their faces might mirror recognition,
A quiet knowledge of their destination.
A trodden path
Not to be measured
In these dusty footprints
Or the weary paces of driven animals,
But in the march of stars and seasons,
The ceaseless steps of years,
Eroding rocks, scouring gorge and watercourse:
The huge journeys of time.

Each seeing fully, in that moment
Of indrawn breath and wonder,
The other's unknown secret:
    The mother of the prophet,
    The great-grandmother of kings.

Reflection

It is possible to imagine that Ruth and Hannah were contemporaries: both women are crucial to the unfolding of purposes far greater than they could imagine. A barren woman, blessed, after grief and longing, with a child who will be the prophet central to Israel's future as a monarchy. An alien woman, finding refuge in Bethlehem, who will be named in the genealogy of David and of the One who comes, a thousand years later, Jesus Christ.

- *What seems especially significant in the life experiences of these two women and the way they are woven into the story of the future Messiah's coming?*

- *All encounters have the potential for sacred significance: 'Christ in eyes of friend and stranger'. How can we become more aware of this?*

- *Biblical references to explore: The Book of Ruth; I Samuel 1, 2:1– 10, 16; Matthew 1:1–17.*

AN ARROW IN THE HAND

I did not think that I would live so long, long enough to see him grow to manhood. So many years! But I know that very soon now, he will leave, and he will never return. As an arrow does not return to the bow.

Since he was scarcely able to walk without a mother's hand to hold him, he would go to the edge of the village and beyond, and gaze out over the bare hills as though the scrub and thorn had already snagged him with their fingers, the graze of the rocks had brothered him with rough touches of comradeship. He was always alone, and the wind's voice called him more urgently than mine, even from infancy. At the breast he would startle, stare at me as though he were a stranger, and then his head would turn to the breeze hushing through the window, or to the white light of the moon. I sometimes thought that he drank more than my milk. He drank from the wildness that called him: the air that played on his skin, the sounds of the distant herds of goats, the starlight that burned in the blue-black sky.

He knew his father, but only for those years when a child grows towards early manhood. My husband was older than I, always gentle and faithful. I remember him, long ago in the first weeks and months of our marriage, teaching me how to read the letters he wrote with a twig in the dust of the yard behind our house. So that, long after, I could speak when they asked me, and say the name. But years had passed since those early days, and we had ceased to dream, ceased to play at letters scribbled in the dust. But we did dream together once, long ago, before my body dried up and failed, and there was no more hope of spring. We did dream of children who would come to complete our lives, to bless and honour us: sons to walk in their father's footsteps, daughters to come close to me in the day by day lessons of the home. Baking the bread, gathering herbs, fetching the water to wash and cook and clean. And one day bringing children of their own to gather around us. The happy quiverful of life.

At first it hardly matters. You are a wife, and there are so many things to learn. The strange intimacy of another's body and the pain and pride of that shy first knowing. For weeks, months, to know with delight that the childhood games you played of housework and cooking only a few years before are now the truth of you. A wife now, and wife to a good and respected man, who kept the Law with reverence and love, not duty and fear. The Festivals would draw us eagerly to Jerusalem where after years of turmoil and oppression, the Temple was being rebuilt, the people free to worship within the limits set by Rome. There was always the happy reunion of family and friends, cousins from the north, bringing their children. In that first year, all is pride and happiness. But then the months begin to turn and they look at you, the women of the village, the relatives and friends met at the Festivals, they look at you, expecting to see the rounding of the belly, the hand to the back, the surge of breasts. They smile at first, with kindness and words to take the shame away. It won't be long. Sometimes it takes a little while. Kind words that sting. And in the home, a puzzled husband, hiding his disappointment, relieved to be called to Jerusalem to fulfil the duties required at the Temple. And leaving you alone.

Slowly, it is as if you lose your youth and then your hopes. I do not know who spoke it first. That biting, bitter word. 'Barren.' I was walking back from the well, the water jar high on my shoulder. A scuffle of sandals behind me, and two women talking, whispering: 'She's barren.' Perhaps they meant me to hear. 'Six years married and no babies, not even a still-born.' Every month that flow of blood that told me of my own emptiness. And another time, walking past a neighbour's door, the voices sniggering: 'of course, he's older than her. No life in him, dried up, like the streams in high summer.' And others would turn from you as they saw you pass and shrink into their doorways lest your shadow brought bad luck and hindered their desired conception. You learn to walk on, don't falter, walk home, shift the heavy jar to the floor, light the fire with twigs and knead the flour and oil together to make the flat bread ready to bake on the stone. Only then, when you sit back, knowing the work has been done, only then, when there is nothing to hold the attention of the mind and hand and eyes, only then do the tears come.

So it passed. Twelve years, and I knew myself to be dead within, dead within my womb, dead within my heart, whilst my husband grew grey with disappointment. How do you sustain belief when all the teaching of the Law, the Prophets and the Psalms tells you that children are a gift from the Lord? What had we done, not to be blessed? Why were there no olive branches around our table? Why was the quiver of our life empty? There is a time when these questions are raw and devouring, when you cannot bear to be together to see the reproach in each other's eyes; when it is no comfort to draw together in the quiet darkness. The silent separate weeping of strangers. Nothing but the habits of his faith and duty gave us a path through this trackless, endless desert.

Yet the passing of slow years surprises you as they bring healing of a sort. Spring comes, not as a mockery of courtship and birth, but as the sound of birds, the flight of swallows returning, the breaking of leaf. And it is beautiful again. You are no longer a young woman, no longer the object of scorn, no longer pitied by older women, mocked by younger ones. You understand with new compassion that it is their fear that makes them sneer, their fear that childlessness may be their portion, that they too might carry the reproach of a barren womb. The heaviness of an emptiness. And in our marriage, kindness, gentleness, a slow growing of a different sort of love, and comfort as we sensed that faith and desperate hope were still holding us safe in God, that we were not forgotten.

So I took my place alongside others in the village, rejoicing at the births of babies born to women thirty years younger than I, comforting those who were in grief. And the shame of my barrenness gave way to something else: a sense of being gathered into the community, accepted. For my husband also, devout in all his duties in the Temple, there came a stronger certainty, a deeper knowing in his innermost being that this life of ours was not in vain. We would go together to Jerusalem, familiar figures ourselves in the worshipping crowds, and there would be others, the old widow who watched and waited all her days in the Court of the Women, never leaving it, some said, and Simeon, far older than my husband. We saw them watching, waiting, and the whisper of faith came to us: the One awaited, the Messiah, is coming.

I did not travel with him to Jerusalem that year. For some while, I had been oppressed with a great weariness, with sweats at night, and all too ready tears. My body's mocking cycle of blood had ended, and with it any faint hope I might have had. He went alone to that great encounter with an Angel and a promise. When he returned one evening, speechless, dazed, bewildered with joy, he was pursued by an eager crowd. The buzz of it brought me to the door, my hands white with flour. They thrust him in, stumbling over their words of visions and angels, signs. Miracles. I could not grasp their meaning, and he could not tell me then. But when they left, he took me in his arms in silent eagerness, gesturing, pointing to myself, to the bed place behind the curtain, and leading me there with that same throbbing sense of shy delight that we had known thirty years before. That same hope, that same wonder of true knowing, true oneness. I thought it had been forgotten. The next day, early in the brightness of a clear dawn, we awoke like young lovers, dressing hastily and taking a handful of figs and raisins to eat. He brought me into the corner of the yard, and there in the dust, he wrote for me as he used to do, and the letters surfaced from my memory and formed sounds and then words as he scratched them, and I understood.

I hid away. Zechariah, silent, radiant, returned to his work, whilst I kept the secret of my swelling body hidden. Perhaps I was afraid. Afraid that I was too old to carry this baby safely. Afraid of the gossip of my neighbours, their misunderstanding, even their rudeness, the jokes that are made of older couples' intimacy. I was afraid of every step, lest I should stumble.

Then Mary came, my young relative from Nazareth, and all was known and all was understood between us. And my baby, restless before, leapt at her coming. She stayed with me for three months, in much need herself of a place of shelter and peace, as old then as I had been when I first married. There was no one else who could have understood or shared so much; with her beside me I began to go about the village and be noticed, and I found the miracle of my neighbours' kindness. She left me just before my baby was born. And after the birth, the neighbours were pressing in to show me their goodness of heart and celebrate with me. So we came to name the child, my husband silent beside me, but I knew his name. My husband and I had shared that secret, drawn in the dust, nine months before: 'His name is John.'

We knew by the Angel's words and the sign given, that he would be a prophet, the one who would go before the Messiah. Our son. Our delight and joy. These things are known among you, words and memories handed down, but you cannot know the years of his growing, the death of his father, the waiting in my old age for all things to be fulfilled. We met sometimes, Mary and I, to share as no others could, the mystery and wonder of our children. We met at the great Feasts in Jerusalem, a great gathering of kinsfolk, and at other times, watching our sons grow up as cousins, playing, laughing, chasing one another on the hillside. But as time went on, my son became more solitary, leaving home early in the morning, striding out onto the hills and beyond. When he was a child, my husband tried to accompany him, but fell behind as John's stride lengthened. We asked him sometimes what was happening, even reproached him that he gave us such anxiety. He had few words, but they burn me still. Such stern, lonely words. 'I am only at home in the wilderness. That is where I am called to be. There will come a day when I must leave you altogether. Now I must learn to live in blazing heat, in bitter cold. I am a sign to the people, and like my father, there will come a day when I am free to speak. Not until then.'

His father died when our son was fourteen. I live in quietness, all grief spent, and I am old, older than I thought I would ever be. The years pass and it is nearly thirty years since that Angel spoke of his birth, and his conception lifted from me forever the blight of barrenness. Few speak of it now, though once it was the talk of the hill country. Has God really come to visit and redeem us? they asked. Now, few remember, but the story is alive as I tell it to you. And so I know, even as I know my own life is ebbing away, that soon I will not see my son again. Through all these years he returned to us, to join us for simple food, to show his love and respect for us, to learn from his father much of the Scriptures. And then, after his father's death, to see that I am cared for. Even with such restlessness of spirit, he would come.

But he has always been an arrow in the hand, and now the bow is drawn, and he is ready to be sent on that flight, foretold long ago. John, my son. My leaping, striding son, born for the wilderness and the wind of God. I sense now at last that the bow is drawn. And I do not know where the arrow will land. But as it strikes the earth, all will be changed.

Reflection

It seems that there could be no greater reproach in the time of Christ, and in the generations before him, than to be childless. Wives then were supposed to be like fruitful vines, and sons like olive shoots or arrows in the hand of a warrior, and the man who had a full quiver of sons was blessed. Yet it is the barren women who figure so largely in the Story: Sarah, Hannah, and now Elizabeth.

- *Keeping faith despite all sorrow and disappointment is a long haul: what can it develop and what can it destroy in the soul?*
- *A woman such as Elizabeth could find herself excluded from the community. Who do we exclude now? What does inclusivity look like in the community of the church?*
- *Biblical references to explore: Psalms 127 and 128; Luke 1:5–25, 39–45, 57–80.*

WOMEN AT THE EDGE

These women, placed like rocks to turn
The current of a stream that else would dissipate,
Dissolve into marshland, dwindle
    into what might have been.
Not seen, excluded, at the edge,
Who recognised (save God)
The barren womb had nourished faith,
Patience, dreams, long before the pledge,
The miracle of birth?
That stream, running through the hearts
Of alien widow, asylum-seeker,
Childless women, past fertility, girl
At risk of rejection by all who knew her.
Who could anticipate
That these would form the riverbed,
The watercourse, flowing from the desert,
Bearing on its flood (like Moses)
That even more extraordinary risk,
A baby?
Not even sly Herod or imperial census,
Nor weary journey and unwelcome
Can hinder this,
This coming entry of the Creator
To his world.

Reflection

'Not seen, excluded, at the edge.' Their significance unrecognised, easily for-gotten perhaps, in their day, and for centuries after, although they have their place in scripture.

- Is it hard to recognise the signs of God working in his/her world? Do we need to look to 'the edge', to the marginalised, the powerless, the disenfranchised, to see more clearly what is bringing in the Kingdom?

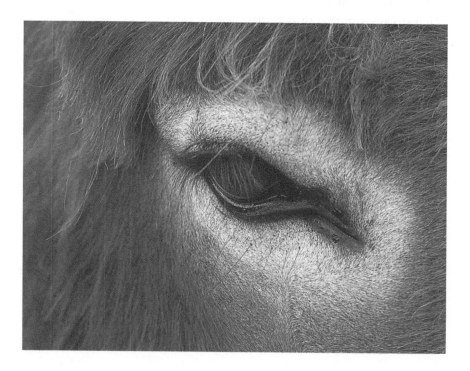

SHAKEN BY THE WIND

When I can stretch them out, the tips of my fingers touch the walls on each side. Rough, damp stone, achingly cold in the darkness. Pressing near, as though the walls might tilt and crush me. The clear air outside, the searching wind from the mountains, the huge swinging patterns of the stars, the blaze of sun, all, all, no longer exist. Water is green and stagnant in the metal dish; food tasteless, clinging dry to the palate and my own spittle barely enough to chew and swallow it. And I shift my position: to stand cramped, to sit hunched, to catch the shaft of grey light that comes in the hours of dawn through the small window high on the wall.

I do not think of her, the woman who sent me here and holds the thread of me between her fingers. She cannot taunt or harm me now. Nor do I fear that sly man, her lover, who visits me secretly at night to hear words that he dare not take into the light with him when he leaves my cell. I stare at these walls, waiting for an ending that I know will come. That I do not fear.

And unfamiliar with the keys and locks of memory, I fumble in my heart to let myself re-admit the past.

Our mothers were very close, that I remember. The warmth of them, a gaiety of spirit as they visited one another, sitting together, talking quietly, laughing sometimes, their hands busy with preparation for the meal or the making and mending of clothes. Singing songs that dated back to the shared year of our birth. Reciting, teaching us. Each holding what I see now was a great secret of gladness and delight. And a deep contentment in each other's company. Yet my mother saw little of her after I reached twelve, and my father died a few years later. From the day of his death she became weary with age and was longing, I think, to follow him. But she watched over me faithfully until I was old enough to survive alone. She knew or guessed my destiny and set me free to explore, to live out under the stars and sky, in the uninhabited places. I cannot imagine now what that cost her. I did not notice then. I last saw her more than a year ago and she was very old, very weak except in spirit. I do not know if she is still alive. But then, all those years ago, before I left home for the last time, I was an earnest student, carefully taught, memorising all the traditions – and running reckless, the neighbours said, over the goat paths of the hill country until I felt that I knew the rocks and scrub of the landscape, the secret springs and streams, better than I knew the yard of my own home. I herded goats, harvested olives and vines for neighbours, learned how to lean into the plough to break up the stony ground and lay it bare for the seed. But all the time, knowing that one day I would leave all this. That I would walk away into the edge of things, and live there, eating and drinking the wind and the wildness, and waiting.

I knew who I was waiting for. As children we had played together, chasing around the trees, screaming in excitement as we splashed through the streams, scooping up handfuls of brilliant water to splatter one another. Then wrestling until we collapsed breathless in the dust and carried our bruises and scratches home to be fussed over, comforted and then forgotten in the warmth of food and shelter.

A happy childhood. Yet great differences came between us. I was serious beyond my years, an isolate, craving the rigours of the desert landscape, matching my body against the starkness of the scything cold under the bright stars, the heaviness of the sun's heat at the height of the day. The words of Law and prophecy devoured me. I craved the disciplines, withdrawing more and more from relationship, from indulgence, from temptation, until without realising it I had left my mother and my home empty and lived in the desert east of the Jordan. I had been in awe of him, younger though he was, in awe of his profound peace. The sense of depth, the secret energy of his faith, his quiet steady assurance of mission. But his path through childhood and into youth was one of friendship, laughter, playfulness. What I struggled for – the earnestness of a walk with God, the prophetic calling, the passion and anger that would denounce the wickedness of the age and turn a nation back to righteousness – he took with ease, as you would take ripe fruit from a tree. 'Yes,' he would say, smiling. 'But there is more. The Kingdom is more than judgement. It is grace.' I did not understand, then or now. I knew that he was God-marked, so close to God in his walking that one day he would stride into the very heart of the nation and begin a ministry like no other to call the people back to God.

Under the wilderness skies, passionate words filled my mouth as my call came to me: to challenge, to call for repentance, to baptise, to defy the religious rulers who had compromised with the politics of Herod Antipas and Rome. To call for crooked paths to be made straight, for mountains of arrogance to be brought low. The crowds came. Curiosity for the spectacle brought many. Some came desperate for renewal, eager to be baptised, to walk a new path, to seek the restoration of the Kingdom. The months went by: all was in preparation for his coming.

Then, I saw him, and knew him as he walked towards me, though we had not talked for many months. I knew this time, this moment, was his: the restoring of the Kingdom. His steps retraced the nation's history as he came down the valley to the Jordan. And I identified him as the One promised, the One about whom the prophets had spoken, the One who would winnow the chaff from the wheat, lay the axe to the root of the tree. Bring the promised judgement and the restoration of Israel. Baptise with the terrible energy of fire. And I was unworthy to untie his sandals.

But what I saw, what he said, demolished me. I saw an awful simplicity, a vulnerability. A lamb, high-stepping over the rocks towards me with that same energy of old, yet carrying already the knowledge of sorrow and sin. 'Look,' I said, not knowing what it might mean. 'The Lamb of God, who takes away the sin of the world.' Not the sin of Israel. That is what I would rather have said. Nor the scapegoat of the Day of Atonement. Something new, something alive and charged with life. Then he came to me, to be baptised. 'To fulfil all righteousness,' he said, seriously, but his eyes were laughing. And I remembered the games of our childhood, and ducked him beneath the water, splashing him with its brightness in the dazzle of the sunshine. But as he turned from me, waist-deep in the pool, I saw the waters running towards him, from way north beyond the Syrian border, water from all the tributaries of the Jordan, deep calling to deep, running over the stones of the riverbed, and bloodied from the past slaughter of tribe against tribe, army against army. Bloodied, too, I saw, with dreadful vision, with the ceaseless warfare of the generations that would follow us, flowing down from the northern heights to run south to the Dead Sea. And he waded through its flow. Then, as he stepped into the shallows and onto the bank, I saw the water running fresh again, the stain vanished as though it had never been.

Then a dove came to him, and I heard the Fathering voice, and the love.

Saw the dove, resting on him.

I did not see him after that. He increased, I decreased, and that is right. And yet I feel, as I remember those days, a deep strangeness between us now. I hear of his words. You visit me with news that he preaches, teaches, heals. Yet no triumphant mission that overthrows the rulers, drives out the corruption of the age. Recalls the people to a jealous God. So I said, ask him, for I have lost my certainty. Ask him, 'Are you the One?'

Your answer shakes me. The blind see. The lame walk. Lepers are whole again. The poor hear good news. The signs of the Messiah. Blessed are those who do not fall away because of me. And so I must begin again. To seek to understand, to see clearly in a place where there is no light, where there is no wind to stir the spirit.

So I set myself, in the grey half-light of each day, and in the blank darkness as night falls, to remember, to trace the river back to its spring. To recall the songs and stories taught us as children. Their chant, half-murmuring song, half-whispered story, comes to me again out of the past into this emptiness of the heart. My own father's song as my mother sung it with her cousin, long ago. He has visited and redeemed his people. A visitor, a guest. And we a nation trampled under the heavy feet of conquerors, invaders. How can such a one claim his Kingdom, restore his people?

The air changes.

A door has opened at the head of the stairs and the breeze touches me, a coolness that for a moment carries the scent of herb and animal, the outside world. The stench of my own clothes and body, the stale and stinking air of the prison, of all of us stifled here, is ruffled and scattered just for a moment by the sweetness of that breath. Then I hear the silence, the way birds fall quiet before the storm, the earth holds its breath before rain. The secret of the jail, the instinctive hush of prisoners before even the first footsteps of the guard slam down the stone stairs, rhythmic, remorseless. Grinding the heavy keys and latch of my door, fastening the chains at wrist and ankles, taking me at last into the upper air.

Freshness of the light wind. Huge night sky visible above the courtyard wall.

Beyond the animal fear, which trembles in my legs and dries my mouth, I feel a great and sudden gladness.

Reflection

John is, perhaps, not an easy figure to empathise with: his tough, outspoken words, reminiscent of the Old rather than the New Testament message; his alien appearance and rigorous lifestyle – it would be difficult to know how he might fit into our 21st century Western lives if he came striding down the high street. Yet, as a child, he was a joy and delight to his parents, desired beyond words, the fulfilment of their most anguished hopes. One day he must have walked away into the wilderness for good, and I've tried to imagine that in the previous story. Now, he speaks to us from a place of vulnerability, and maybe we can draw closer to him there.

- *John speaks to us from the wild places, from the edge, from intimate dwelling with herb and scrub, creatures and weathering.*

What elements of wilderness do we most value, and what do they tell us of God? What must it have been like for John to be imprisoned?

- *Why does he not understand the words and works of the cousin for whom he had prepared the way? In what ways can there be a tension between righteousness and mercy, compassion and justice, and how do we resolve it – in society, in churches, in ourselves?*
- *Biblical references to explore: Luke 3:1–20; 7:18–28; Matthew 14:1–14.*

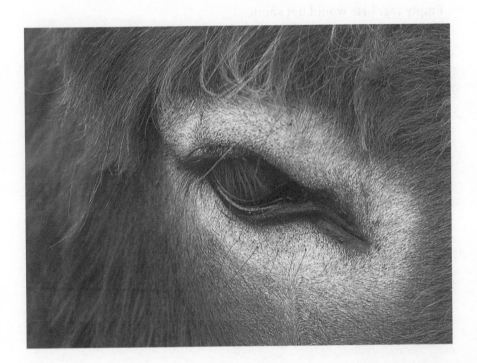

HIS WORDS

What if John should come, treading the wilderness
Of ruined forest, raped, incinerated homes,
Bombed cities? Or here,
Trampling the wretched grass,
By burnt-out cars and bags of leaking rubbish:
Estates, barren with neglect,
The windows blind, meaningless
Words scrawled in mere
Empty rage? He would not shout
But weep for pity, for the loss
Of hope, the helplessness.

He cries out, Turn the hearts of the fathers
To the children! Standing
Beneath the window, outside the door
Where the child cowers at the father's voice.
He strides
Beneath the blackened tower
Of Grenfell and wherever justice hides
Behind bureaucracy. Turn the hearts
Of leaders to their people!
Governments to the poor,
Employers to their workers,
The fathers of nations to the helpless,

The displaced, thrust into the wasteland
Of the world.
His words are hurled
Across the centuries. Hear them.

Reflection

John challenges us to consider the role of the prophet, and to ask: 'Who are the prophets of our day, and what words are they speaking?' I don't think they are necessarily always found in the Church.

- *Do you? ...*

When I read about John, I am most moved by the phrase, 'Turn the hearts of the fathers to the children' (Luke 1:17). I find it disturbingly relevant and so the poem has these words at its heart. I have referenced the Grenfell fire because it seems to me emblematic of the ways in which terrible suffering is brought about by greed and negligence and the vulnerable left without recompense or justice.

I have considered what John's prophetic voice might be speaking today.

- *What would you add or emphasise? ...*

CHRISTMAS

WHEN THE TIME HAD FULLY COME

An indrawn breath of waiting.
Imminence so close, so urgent,
Resembling blood, throbbing in the heart,
Beating in the throat.
Reverberating silently for those with ears to hear.

Like a quickening in her own long-widowed womb,
A word upholds her now, watchful for his coming.
And an old man, sleepless with longing, raises
Eager eyes to heaven.

Far away, a gathering of the wise
Has searched the skies for guidance
Exceeding all their past predictions
Of this vast sweep of dazzling constellations.

The imperial seal is pressed into ready wax.
A hundred emissaries ride to command a census.
In far-off provinces, indifferent to Rome,
Wearied people shrug and stir,
Beginning journeys that return them to their birth.

In his palace a king stares into the shadowed corners
Of his mind, demanding light
To banish darkness and its terrors,
Fearing to eat the poisoned fruit that he himself has sown.

Among their restless flock, heavy now with lamb,
Shepherds listen for that first tremulous bleat of birth
And watch and wait for dawn to dull the stars,
Ushering the sun over the eastern hills.

And in a northern town, an anxious husband watches
His young wife smooth and fold some linen strips into their pack,
Before her slow and gravid steps
Will take her south beside him.

Reflection

The poem's title is taken from a quotation (Galatians 4:4). We can wonder at the perfect timing of God, the coming together of so many elements of the story, the context of comparative peace and freedom to travel in the Empire. But we can also see that the perfect timing of this transformative event is made up of so many small and trivial things. People whose names are forgotten, an insignificant town, a tedious journey. Even the celebrity is a petty tyrant of a king, desperate to keep usurpation at bay.

- *Is it the outwardly great things of life that have been the most significant in the journey of faith, or the seemingly trivial? Have you seen ways in which the small, the insignificant things have led to breakthrough? Are there examples you could explore?*
- *Why has the church been so corrupted by power and earthly sway, when we see that God works so differently? What is power?*

ALL STATIONS TO KING'S CROSS

This is a poem that could work in performance at a Christmas Service.

Travelling light – a grabbed bag –
Slammed door –
'You don't belong here no more!
Get out!' – cheap single, no seat,
No reservation, heading south,
London station.
What'll we do? *Sign on.*
What else? *Find shelter.*
A hostel maybe, just for the night.
Someone might help. *They might.*
Don't leave me. I don't know our destination.
Just, London station.

    The baby will come. Moves. Demands its life.

Don't let it come now, not there,
Not crouched in this angle of a dark stair
Slick with trampled filth and stench.
Not born among these shuffling homeless:
Drunks, whores, pimps, predators,
Waiting, collecting the spent tickets of lives.

    Who else travels this journey?
    This ancient route of shame and isolation.
    Who is alongside the destitute and cast out,
    Bureaucracy-burdened? Asylum-seeking?

Who cares or shares the slammed door,
The bitter names and curses,
The birth in a dark corner?

A birth of light into dark,
Weighted now with the heaviness of flesh.
A mother, weary with knowledge
That dissects the heart,
Holding a mystery:
Arrival and departure,
All in this instant.

Edinburgh, Berwick, Newcastle, York,
Doncaster, Peterborough, Nazareth, Bethlehem, Jerusalem.
All stations.
  All Stations of the Nativity
  End at King's Cross.

Reflection

- *What do you make of the last stanza?*

  Edinburgh, Berwick, Newcastle, York,
  Doncaster, Peterborough, Nazareth, Bethlehem, Jerusalem.
  All stations.
    All Stations of the Nativity
    End at King's Cross.

UNIMAGINABLE

The slung weight of him,
Carried for stumbling miles.
The arrival, unwelcomed,
And the roofless, ruthless search for somewhere
To lie, to crouch, to shelter them
For the tearing open of his birth, his entry
To an indifferent world
(As he would, one day, bear
The weight of his own means of death
And the torn wounding of his departure).
Her husband's shoulder, all his instincts
Turning from the uncleanness
Of it, the blood, the woman's mysteries,
Yet all his tenderness
Turning to her and her struggle, and labouring with her,
Crafting from the raw trunk, the planed, smooth,
Silken beauty of the birth.
A woman's kindness, coming at last with the sooth
Of water, washing, cleansing, assuaging thirst.
His nuzzling thirst, for this time, too, assuaged,
His body stilled and swathed in wraps of linen.
Then shepherds come, familiar with birth,
With stabling, trodden straw and blood and weary labour,
But now uncertain, sharing a bewildered wonder
Of dazzling light in awkward, gestured words.

She could not imagine us, this,
Our 'now'. How could she?
She would not recognise our annual presentation
Of her story.
Angels, clustering in tinselled fairy costumes,
The pet shop straw, the pink doll
Held in the child's uncertain clasp,
An unwilling Joseph's arm around her.
Shepherds, striped and tea-towelled,
And kings with gilded cardboard crowns.

Or would she? Not the Nativity
Played a thousand ways, but the grave hilarity,
The joy, the moment's magic of it. The children's eyes
Wondering. The words spoken
Again and again, 'Peace on earth',
'A Saviour born to you'. This she might recognise,
And marvel, as we do,
At their enduring freshness, their yearning hope
Of peace. Their ageless promise of new birth,
In every generation.

Reflection

*What would Mary recognise in our Nativity plays? We are so 'familiar'
with the Christmas story that its grim details – the tough journey while
heavily pregnant, the terrible risk of being unmarried, the birth in a shed –
are often sanitised or sentimentalised.*

- *Why – despite all the familiarity of the words, the jingling super-
  market carols, the stumbling renditions of their lines by shy
  children in school performances – does this story of this birth still
  touch all our deepest yearnings, our half-forgotten dreams?*

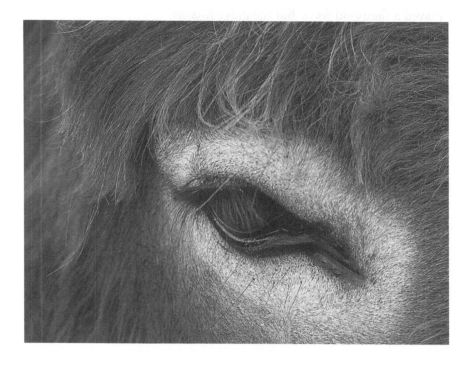

JUST LIKE ONE OF US

A clear night. Quiet. Watchful, you might say, as though something might happen. So we stayed awake, restless even when we weren't on watch, although the sheep were calm enough, drowsy as though a great heaviness had fallen on them. A sudden far burst of light, which travelled slowly over the hills, nearer, nearer – and as it came it blinded us. And we stumbled to our feet, clutching each other, helpless. Then, as we slowly opened our eyes, careful, terrified lest the light would burn them in their sockets, we found we could see, and the night sky was filled with brightness. The soft glory of early-morning light before the sun has risen. Gold, white, and then as we looked, we could see colours. I don't have the words, though I saw once, in the city market, dyed cloth fit for a prince, purple and scarlet, but this was like the colours of sunset, the colours of dawn and the rainbow all mingled and woven, and figures that seemed to dance, some slow, some as fast as lightning. We dropped to our knees and some cried out with fear, hiding our eyes because it was too beautiful for us, too wonderful for us to see, like a forbidden thing, like the stories they tell of the Holy of Holies that only the High Priest may enter. But this *was* for us to see. The glory. The Voice told us. Out of the dance came voices, singing. Heaven and earth touching, and peace on earth, the favour of God resting on men. I tell you, you've never known what it is to live with the fear of war and the memory of war, told to you from childhood. With the tramp of soldiers' feet occupying the country, taking over our land. It's settled now. You barely notice. Live and let live, except for the taxes. But then, the promise of peace! And after that the Voice. For you, it said. The One who will save you. Messiah. Go and find him, go into Bethlehem. And then it felt like madness, that laughter that filled the skies and overtook us so that we laughed too. He's all swaddled up and lying in a manger. Just like one of us. Poor, and making do with whatever is at hand. Go, the Voice said, as we stood and gaped. Hurry. And so we scrambled away, but not before we saw an amazing thing. That glory, they sung about, that glory that filled the skies, it touched us. I saw old Eliab, so patient with labouring sheep, and his grandson Jos, who was learning alongside him. And Samuel, brave and strong when the robbers came, and Zachary, skilled at shearing time, I saw them all and the glory rested on them and seemed to fill them for a moment so that they became ... well, true. Their true selves. That's the best I can do to explain.

So, we tumbled down the stony paths to Bethlehem with the Voice in our ears and the fading glory of the angels over our heads. Yes, we found him, the baby, lying in a manger, with cloths around his tiny body and protecting him from the sharpness of the husks of the straw. So still, so small. We felt clumsy and awkward, stinking of the smell of sheep and unwashed, greasy clothes, but that young mother and her husband welcomed us in as though we were their special visitors. We told our story, and they nodded as though they already knew and would remember, and we knelt and saw, and wept, and laughed, and Eliab reached out his forefinger and gently touched the sleeping baby's cheek. Then a long, long time later it seemed, we realised just how weary that young mother must be and crept away, suddenly aware of our flock abandoned on the hillside. But when we found them, all was well. Some sleeping, some slowly grinding the sparse grass of the hillside. The ewes heavy with lamb. We counted them and found that nothing had been lost. But overhead, no trace of that brilliant light, those voices that had filled the bowl of the hills. I thought, when they came, they must have split the roof of the sky, but when I looked it was whole again and the birds were waking and the sky turning from darkness to the first grey hints of light. We spoke of nothing else – how could we? We told of the marvel to families, to friends, to anyone who would listen, and the story was told and retold for years, though now, there are few who would remember.

Shepherds are despised, mostly. Yet we watch and wait, and we neither slumber nor sleep. You see, we know the songs, the old songs. Maybe we know God in ways that the priests and rabbis have forgotten. David was one of us, David the great king, David whose heir would be the Messiah one day. He will feed his flock like a shepherd, the prophecies tell us, and carry the lambs and lead the burdened ewes gently. One of us. That is our secret, our hope. They despise us because we do not keep the Sabbath. Well, the saying is, 'wolves and robbers know no Sabbath'. And that's true. The thieves who steal on the Sabbath are the worst kind of thief, so we keep watch all hours, all weathers.

Yes, I've been to Jerusalem. Only once. I went with Zachary and Jos, long ago, when I was a young man, keen to see the sights. We were taking the pick of the flock for the great Passover Festival. Other owners would tell their shepherds to choose the weak and diseased and hide them among the stronger ones. But not our master. We took firstborn lambs in their strength and walked with them, letting them graze and drink until we saw the walls and towers, and the sun glinting on the marble of Herod's temple and we knew our journey, and their journey, was over. But I hated the noise and stench of the city. The crowds, the shouting, the clash and stamp of armed men, the get-out-of-my-way behaviour of the religious leaders. The sad beggars at street corners, the blind, the crippled. I never went again. I knew then that I belonged in the clear air, under open skies and all weathers, however harsh.

What happened to that family, to the baby? I heard that they fled from Bethlehem after the visit of strangers from eastern lands, and that soldiers sent from Herod came too late to find the child, but not too late to slaughter any other little boys they found. That was the kind of king he was. Cruel, wicked. That little family must have become wanderers, homeless, like so many under the Romans and under Herod's rule. Drifting on the roads, hoping for refuge. Who knows? I can tell you how long ago it was. Every year, since then, I've put a notch on my crook, counting the seasons round: harvest and the fall of leaf, the bare winter, lambing and the awakening of spring, the fullness of summer: each year, another notch. And there are thirty now. And of those shepherds that heard and saw that marvel, I am the only one left, and I am old. Not in years, perhaps, though more than fifty is a good age, but my body is old. Life on those raw hillsides sucks the life out of you, and I can no longer hold and turn a sheep for shearing. So I have come down to the village, to the small house where my wife raised the children and waited for me to come to her for the few days that I had leave to come. My eldest son and his wife care for me now, as I cannot move easily from the bed they have made for me. They are kind and patient. 'Abba', they both call me. My son would have made a good shepherd, but he chose a different path, showing a talent for mending and making and I was able to ask the master to help with his apprenticeship, and now he is a potter. Each day they help me to rise and eat, and if the weather is gentle I sit outside and remember, and I tell my grandson what I have told you. And he smiles and listens, though I have told him many times.

But I cannot believe that the story is over. Every evening, before I settle to sleep, I stand at the doorway leaning on my staff, this crook, and turn my eyes to the night sky, and I watch, and wait.

Reflection

- *In giving the shepherd a voice, we're listening in our imaginations to someone who was voiceless in the society of his time. Who are the voiceless ones now, and are they privy to the secrets of God, do you think?*
- *The shepherd cannot believe that the story is over and so he watches and waits. He might hear of the adult Jesus beginning his ministry. Is watching and waiting something that is meaningful to us, and if so, what are we waiting for, and what are the signs of hope?*
- *Biblical reference to explore: Luke 2:8–2*

EPIPHANY

MIRAGE

Stories blow along the ancient travellers' routes like uprooted bushes in the desert, like dust clouds that spiral and dance in gusts of sharp, hot, snapping wind. Or they hover like mirages, full of promise, beckoning forward to nothing. To a place of no-arrival.

But there was a story once, and it has grown in the telling, passing from traveller to traveller, shifting its shape and meaning: there was a story once, and I was part of it, following a mirage, tugged by the desert wind. Nearly a lifetime ago, but I remember more now, and understand a little, and it seems right to tell of it and give it place and time before the story whisks away into legend or becomes like the tales we tell to children, and loses all its truth.

You would not recognise me. Not then. You see me now in the consulting room, or in the hours of pain and fear when you call for me, and I move to reassure, to diagnose, to treat whenever possible. To touch, to establish that bond of unspoken kinship with you, to take the dread of suffering and death into myself and hold it if I can. I learned those things. That touch is more than words. That the eyes speak more than the voice. That the body is a marvellous thing that heals itself in so many situations. Until a whisper of mortality slips into the ears of the soul, and takes up its hiding place there. I learned those things, watching, serving, holding, long before I trained for medicine. I learned them as I saw the sickness grow in him and the spirit of the man burn as he fought to make the long journey, consuming energy, life itself, as he travelled.

I was fifteen. A time when everything is observed with fierce concentration, and felt with the sharpness of anguish, the simplicity of devotion. My mother and I had been born into his service, and when he was insistent that he must go, must carry the frailty of himself on this search, I went with him. I could care for the animals and secure places for us to stay. And more, I could nurse him and give him the care that he needed and keep hidden from the prying eyes of other travellers the desperate nature of his need. My mother showed me the measure of opium to give him when the pain became excruciating. She spoke with me of the needs that might come as he grew weaker: how to wash him, to enable him to relieve himself, to find food that might be digestible, to make sure that there was always water or water mixed with wine. And in telling me, she wept, for he was loved and honoured, and she knew he would not return. Before we left he handed us both the documents that gave us freedom and more than enough financial provision to make a home and livelihood. What I did not know then was that he had set up a fund for me to gain a training, for he had already ensured that I could read and write. So I could be a lawyer or a doctor, a banker or an engineer. The stigma of slavery utterly gone.

'We go first to meet old friends,' he said, shaking out the reins of his horse and smiling for a moment without a shadow of pain or age. 'Friends I studied with, long ago. Letters have come and gone between us all this time, but we have not met in thirty years. But now. Now.' And his thoughts drifted away into some mystery, some memory perhaps that I could not follow, and then he smiled again, and with an energy I had never seen, touched his heels to his horse's flanks and moved ahead of me to the town gate and the beginning of the trade route west.

We kept to clear tracks across the barren country, following in the dust of other travellers, the slots of hooves and wheels, but keeping separate. Not aloof: he was not a proud man, but separate, conserving energy, hiding the greyness of pain, the slumped weariness at the end of each day.

At nightfall, I found us lodgings, brought him food and drink, then slept outside his door, or with the animals, his horse and mine and the mule that carried the burden of our clothes and necessaries.

So we journeyed. A good day would take us forward twenty miles, some days only five. And always the sun burned above us, reaching such a height of power at noon it was as if it pressed us to the ground with a giant's fist. At night, the heat of the day fled away and sheer cold gripped us. The darkness was studded with astonishing stars whose patterns moved ceaselessly, tirelessly across the dome of the sky.

Many weeks later, in the haze of early evening, we came to a city with towers and high walls faintly tinged by the pink and orange of a sun that slid reluctantly from the sky. The heat of the day, held in its stone and dust, the smells of cooking, the raucousness of voices smote us. After the silence, the separateness, it shocked me, though something in my youth longed to explore, to follow the beckoning trails of alleys and run my fingers through the displays of the market – silks and spices and fruits. Now, as at the beginning, I saw a new energy in him, and he beckoned me forward to follow him. We rode through a sequence of winding lanes between white walls until we came to an open courtyard, a fountain playing in a marble pool, scurrying servants coming to us to take the horses, and a shout of welcome from the doorway as though the master of the house had spent his day looking out for us. Jealous, I could not let them help him from his horse, and steadied him until he was able to stand and move forward to the greeting that awaited him – his host running down the steps to him and they embraced and kissed and wept like brothers.

He knew. He turned and saw me clutching the reins of the mule, my face stubborn, and called me over. 'My faithful Azir,' he said, gently. 'He has supported me on this long journey.' Then his face lost all colour, and as he fell we caught him and carried him into the house and to his room.

All that night he slept fitfully, and I watched him and wiped his forehead, giving him water mixed with wine to sip whenever he woke. I fell asleep as dawn's promise crept into the high window above his head, then jolted awake as he stirred and smiled, his eyes full of youth again despite the wretchedness of his body. Food and drink were brought, and he was able to wash and dress and stand unsupported.

As we left his bedchamber we found his friend pacing the corridor, and again, that eagerness, that comradeship, revived him. 'Come with me,' he said, and leant on my arm and we walked down the long marble hall to the courtyard, and he sat with his friend talking. Old stories, old laughter, and then, suddenly, the conversation turned. Turned to a gravity and complexity that I could not follow, and by that time my eyes were heavy with the sleep lost in the night, and with the many watchful nights that had preceded it. I found myself nodding forward, catching fragments only of talk that seemed to be of calculations, times and distances, with charts of huge patterns spread upon the low table. Suddenly, the clatter of hooves at the gateway and an urgent, demanding voice, swift steps across the courtyard and a messenger carrying a scroll. My master's friend rose to his full height, broke the seals and read the message, turning rapidly to excuse himself, and then to summon horse and give instructions for the care of his guests. 'I will return this evening, I trust,' he said. 'And we should soon be joined by our third friend of those student days! He has travelled the Silk Road from the East, but I had news from him yesterday that he will be with us before nightfall. If I am delayed, you will have much to share.' Then he walked quickly to the gate, mounted the horse held ready for him and rode away.

'He is the king's chief advisor,' I learned. 'Such a summons must be obeyed, most especially now if he is to have leave for the long journey that awaits us.' So I waited, and my master rested in the shade, and the day moved over the courtyard in shortening and lengthening blue-black shadows. As I waited, I pondered: this unknown journey; these friends; their talk, so hard to follow, of the movements of the stars, the geometry of the Greeks, the learning and debate of Alexandria. Then, towards evening, a third traveller, thin and sparse, with deep eyes that read you as he greeted you. And our host returned, weary with responsibilities, and we ate together, and the talk strayed through Greek to Aramaic languages and Latin, with laughter and memories, but with an increasing sense of an approaching climax as the meal ended.

'Now,' said our host, and beckoned us up the winding stairway to a tower where, in the deepening indigo of night, a million stars waited for us, forming themselves into patterns, constellations that these men traced with eager, sweeping arms. Dreamers, wide-eyed and passionate, yet serious in their calculations and with their careful measuring instruments, leaning up against the balustrade to point and gesticulate.

'It was always you,' they said, half laughing, yet tender in their recollections and in their gestures of affection for my master as they turned to him. 'You saw the patterns long ago, and the converging pathways of the stars. And now the time has come.'

'And we must begin our journey, as soon as we are ready,' he answered them. He held my arm closely as we descended the stairs. 'Tomorrow, we ride west, and then south by the old merchants' road. I will need your help to pack, and all your care if I am to travel.' I saw his friends' deep concern as they marked his weakness, the greyness that invaded his face and broke in sweat on his forehead. 'Azir is a son to me,' he said to them. 'He will help me reach our destination. I cannot manage without him.' And he smiled at me even though he was trembling and in much pain.

And so we rode out, in opal light that flowed from the sky as dawn broke, giving ourselves several hours of coolness before the smiting sun forced us to seek refuge. Very little baggage, strapped on horses and the mule, and dull, inconspicuous clothing. Slowly, I came to know and understand a little of my master's friends. I served them all, finding lodging, tending and guarding the animals. The cares of royalty, the burden of his duties, still hung on the first of them. The lines around his mouth and eyes seemed grained with responsibility, his voice strong with a readiness to command, yet always gentle, always courteous to me. The second, whom I had barely met before we set off, was quiet. No, quiet is not enough to describe him. He held silence within himself as though he were a cup, a chalice of stillness. Late into the night under the stars, and sometimes early, even before the dawn, I saw him leave the room or the tent, and pace beneath the dark sky. I watched him once, until I realised that this was too private, too costly for me to see. Sometimes his arms were lifted up as though in prayer or entreaty, or his hands clenched with some great struggle. And there were times when I was tending to my master as he returned, bending his head under the lintel of the door, or stooping at the tent's entrance, and in the faint light I sometimes saw the tracks of tears on his cheeks and glistening in his beard.

They spoke little, as though their agreement was so deep it needed few words. I came to understand their haste, their secrecy. I saw that their journey was the coming together of long roads, separated for a lifetime until these men felt this compulsion, this certain knowledge. A compulsion that had gathered them at last to search the skies for direction and seek with the passion of their youth, the dedication of their age, the One foretold. So much I understood, and gave myself to serve them, to make it possible, I told myself, for my master to succeed in his quest, at whatever cost. And gradually I learned from them how to read the skies and recognise the burning conjunction of stars that called them forward.

And so we came at last, and after many weeks, to the weary, indifferent guards of the border crossing and then to Jerusalem. And here we found a place to stay, and they brought from their packs the clothes of their rank and dignity to dress to greet the King. I waited whilst they sought their royal audience, standing in the marketplace whilst soldiers thrust their way through the crowd, merchants called their wares, blind beggars whimpered as they were shoved to the edge, religious leaders drew aside from the women and the urchins of the streets. Once again the magic of the city, the juxtaposed glamour and wretchedness, the dazzle of goods and trades took hold of my youth, even though I felt weighted with the solemnity of the quest.

It was many hours before they returned, reproaching themselves as fools to have looked in the palace of such a man for the One they sought. And in their haste there was urgency, even a sense of danger, my master finding within himself an extraordinary strength. They changed their clothes, and we rode out quickly and left the city through the South Gate, taking the roads through the hill country. And all night they pointed to that dazzling configuration in the heavens. Until, and at last, they came very early the next day to Bethlehem, a straggling village, hardly a town, of white houses, goats and donkeys tethered at gate posts and olive trees greygreen in the fields. Quiet under the open sky.

Here they seemed to need no guidance, dismounting before a small house, flat-roofed, humble, even poor. I stood, holding the reins, perplexed, whilst they sought in their packs for gifts concealed all this while and never spoken of. My master turned: 'Come. Come with me now. I need your arm. This has been your journey also.' So I looped the reins together hurriedly. Then they knocked on the door, and each one, bowing his head beneath the crossbeam, entered. And I with them.

What can I tell you? There was nothing extraordinary there, yet every-thing. A young woman, hardly older than I; a man, stooping protectively over her. At her breast, covered hastily with a linen cloth, a baby. She turned to see us as we entered, and then brought the baby onto her lap and murmured to her husband as the three old men knelt down before her and her child. The baby, scarcely six weeks old, I think, opened the clear liquid unfocused eyes of babyhood and seemed to gaze at them. There were no words spoken, no movement, not at first. I knelt at the heels of my masters, and watched, sensing mysteries that I could not grasp, not then. And only now, a little. Beneath her eyes, the blue-black semicircles of sleeplessness, and gauntness in the cheeks, but the curve of her mouth was full of tender pride. Her husband's arm encircled her. Square, strong craftsman's hands. A serious, steady face of great kindness. Around them, a home of extreme simplicity with meagre furniture, a bed piled with rugs in the corner, a hearth and cooking pots, shelves, benches.

Then there were words and explanations, phrases of Aramaic that I could barely follow. Their quest. The folly of their visit to Jerusalem. The One, they said, born King of the Jews. Their recognition of his Kingship even in his babyhood. The great patterns of the stars that had brought them here.

But it is this that stays with me.

They brought out their gifts as they spoke, and one by one offered them to the child as he lay in her lap. The one whom I had come to know as Balthazar, the king's advisor, held out a simple circlet of gold, the crown of a prince, I would imagine. The dark eyes of the baby mirrored it in the oil-lamp's light and he reached out wandering hands and arms to take it as it was offered, holding its sullen, gleaming, weighty smoothness and pulling it towards himself, until it rested on his shoulder.

Then Gaspar drew out the casket he had brought and opened its lid, and the heady fragrance of frankincense resin breathed out into the little room, and he, too, leant forward to let the baby touch the gift. The child's mother smiled and gently took the weight of the gold circle from his shoulder to where it could rest alongside him in her lap, as the uncertain, wavering hands of the baby reached for the casket and the old man, weeping, held its weight. And the child brought it to his own little chest, above the heart, and held it there, serene and still for many moments.

Then Melchior, my own master, brought his gift, a precious flask of alabaster, sealed at the neck, made, I guessed then, to hold the oils for anointing at burial, myrrh among them. The alabaster whiteness gleamed in his dark hands, and I marked even at that moment, their fragility and trembling. And as he approached the baby, the child's hands took, not the flask, but his hands, and brought them to his face, his eyes steadfast, drinking, it seemed to me, the face and form of my master as though some strange process of understanding passed between them. Some absorption of his pain and frailty, his mortality, into himself.

We stayed in stillness for a long time. Then the young husband stirred, spoke gently to his wife, and offered bread and wine, olives and figs for our refreshment. Three old men moved stiffly from their knees and we ate and drank in their home, grateful for their kindness. And it seemed that we returned to reality, if reality is what we call it. Until we entered the house I had considered all this journey an old man's quest, a mirage of youth, but I had seen into the truths that lie at the heart of dreams and desires, here in this humble home, and in the wandering hands and eyes of a tiny baby. I had seen these men, amongst the wisest of their generation, give the gift of their lives to this child. Even now, I wonder at it.

We left in the cool of the evening, seeking to stay at the inn; but in the early hours of the morning the lord Gaspar roused us to tell us of his dream, a warning that King Herod would seek our lives and we must not return to the court of Jerusalem. So we did not take the expected route, but rode west to the coast, taking ship at Joppa and setting out for Alexandria.

And there on board ship, my master Melchior lay resting against my shoulder under an awning on deck, his eyes gazing out to the horizon. 'Tell your mother,' he said, 'that I am going home by another way.' Then he thanked me, and said farewell to his friends, and shuddered once, and smiled and died. Gently, carefully, we tended his body, wrapping it in linen, speaking over it words of love and hope before we loosed it to the depths of the Great Sea. We stayed awake much of that night, tracing the stars that directed the helmsman's course, but needing few words, then, or in the days that followed, as we sailed west.

After we landed at Alexandria, we all took different roads. I took the long road home, selling the horse and riding the mule. 'When the time is right,' Balthazar had said to me, 'come to me and I will enable you to train as a doctor.' For I had already spoken of my desire.

So it was, seven years later, that I returned to the city of white walls and the marble courtyard. Since then, I have found myself waiting always for news from Jerusalem. It is more than thirty years since we followed the dream across the desert roads from the east. It is only now, as I tell you, that I know the certainty of its enduring substance.

Reflection

This story of the travellers from the East, and their gifts, is fascinating. It brings to the story of the little family an element of exotic mystery. The Gentiles come and worship. They bring amazing gifts.

- *What does the story of the Wise Men mean to you and what does it add to all the signs and amazement of the story of Jesus' birth and early childhood?*
- *What does it also tell us about human government and the abuse of power? And the extraordinary risk of exposing the vulnerability of a baby, his mother and her husband to the agents of despotism? Why did God take such a risk, do you think?*
- *Biblical reference to explore: Matthew 2:1–18*

AN ANCESTRAL PROMISE

Barely out of girlhood, she had become a wife. Then, so suddenly, a widow.

He had fallen on the hillside, bringing down the goats for milking. Tripped on an unexpectedly dislodged stone, or a slip of pebbles at the edge of the path, and hit his head against a rock. The goats, creatures of habit, driven by the need of their swollen udders, had come down to the small dwelling and she had crouched to milk them, not thinking that her husband lay out on the rocks as the day chilled, his blood stiffening around the wound in his left temple. Only later, when she had prepared supper and the bread that she had baked on the hot stones in front of the fire was blackening, did she go to the doorway and call, frightened now, her voice echoing off the darkening hillside. Late into the evening she had searched for him, calling, calling, clambering up the path to the places he had shown her where the goats found pasture. She had stumbled at last against his body, touching it to find it cold and stiff, then embracing it with cries of desperation.

Widowhood. After seven years of childless marriage. She had felt herself cursed with barrenness for seven years of waiting. Enduring each month her own sense of shame and his disappointment, disappointment that had turned to hidden resentment. Now, as she lay awake, night after night, struggling with grief and fear, she felt a dulling sense of abandonment by God. Her neighbours were kind now. Kinder than their shrugged whisperings that had pursued her slender body as she carried water, purchased flour and oil, wandered alone through the marketplace during the years of her marriage. In the first numb months of widowhood, they helped her to manage the small herd of goats and sell the milk, and often she found gifts of food and wine waiting for her as she returned each evening from the pasture.

Sometimes in those early days, she abandoned the goats on the hillside, and wandered blindly through the cool grey olive groves, crushing yellow sorrel and vivid glossed anemones beneath her angry, stumbling feet. Her hands reached out to grip the twisted ancientness of trunk and branch, forgetting grazed fingers in the compulsion of her cries and questions. The impassive silence of the trees mocked her barren widowhood as their branches bent with fruit. Their elemental secret: oil crushed out of bitterness, eluded her.

In the early years of her marriage, terrible news had come daily from Jerusalem, carried with speed along the roads, finding its way over the hills to remote villages by track and twisting path. Beggars brought it first, and in their wake, fleeing women with their starving, wide-eyed children. Footsore city dwellers, their few possessions strapped to their backs, their older children burdened with loads too heavy for them, the babies and infants crying for food and water. All speechless at first, as though the tale they carried was too ugly, too dreadful to relate. Chaos and breakdown in the streets as the government collapsed and then the terrifying news of invasion by Rome, Israel now ripe to be plucked and stripped of her sovereignty. A brutal siege of the city and then the desecration of the Temple itself, as though the heart of the nation had been ravaged. A ruthless conquering garrison moved through the broken city, demanding, taking, stamping its will, the might of Rome, onto a subject people. Even now, some years later, the horror of it lingered in eyes and trembling hands, and in the question none dared ask, 'Has God forgotten his people?'

Now, from her place of grief, she looked with awakened pity on the desperate incomers who continued to flee to the village. Her home was opened to them, and a small family, a mother and her three children, came to live with her. Ezra, the eldest child, a gangling boy of twelve or so, helped her with the goats, loping alongside her up the hillside. She taught him the names and calls and the best patches of scrub and grass that the animals needed to visit in turn. He learned how to milk them, leaning against them as though to draw comfort from their rough flanks while his thin fingers drew the threads of milk into the pot. The woman helped with the cooking and the cleaning around the house and gradually, as her infant daughter began to stagger around the floor, the two women learned to smile again and share the delight of newly quickened laughter.

She never knew the full story of her guests' lives, only what she could guess from the sudden outbursts of the middle child, quickly hushed, and the muttered torment of the family's nightmares that sometimes roused her from her sleep. A husband done violently to death in defence of his family; the doors of their home smashed open and the children thrust into hiding before the woman was abused. That was what she could piece together. And it stirred Anna beyond her own widowhood to turn again to prayer: not for herself, but for this family entrusted to her and for a nation of many such families, torn by sorrow and suffering and yearning for restoration and healing.

Years passed by in growing, surprising contentment. The children grew to near adulthood and their mother, Miriam, set about arranging the marriages for the two girls. She visited Jerusalem with Ezra to search for relatives, old neighbours, to find again the ties of relationship and security which meant that she might be sure of her daughters' happiness. Ezra was settled in the village, a familiar young man at the small synagogue, a farmer now, who had added to the herd and with the sale of meat, skins and milk had bought land. 'One day,' he told his mother and Anna. 'One day there will be enough for me to marry,' and he asked his mother to begin the delicate negotiations with the family of the young girl he had set his heart on.

Both daughters were found husbands in Jerusalem and their mother moved to be with the youngest, but living on the other side of the city, away from the ruined and now rebuilt streets of their old home. Ezra continued to lodge with Anna until his wedding and then, quite suddenly, even though he made provision for her, she was alone. Frequently, there was news, and much of it happy, of babies and the discovery of old friends and family members who had not been driven away by the Roman occupation but had survived or returned to make a life again. The streets of Jerusalem were uneasy but safe, held in the grip of the occupation and pacified under the puppet ruler Rome had set in place. There was talk that one day even the Temple, trampled and raped as it had been, might be restored to worship and become again the rhythmic heart of the nation.

All of this flowed through Anna's mind. She began to sense something of great moment in her waiting, her watchfulness. It was as though every experience had prepared her for some great event. An event, nameless as yet, but of such magnitude that sometimes, sleepless in the silence of the dark, or walking alone on the hills, she knew herself to be accompanied: there was a voice waiting for her to truly listen, or a figure alongside that her eyes could not quite distinguish. Years ago, in the sorrow of her widowhood and as she heard of the desolation of Jerusalem and the misery of its destitute victims, she had cried out words that she had heard from the Lamentations of the Prophet. Her own forsakenness, the city's violation, the homeless and helpless family that had escaped and come to her were all one in her weeping, and the words that seemed to form in the depths of her womb. There was no comfort, there was only the distress and agony of a people forsaken. But as she had discovered love again and the healing that comes through friendship and acts of kindness, she had found this anguish had turned to prayer. It became the compelling rhythm of her life, urgent yet full of hope. Now, gazing up into the sky's translucency in the early hours of the morning, or watching the slow turning of the nighttime constellations, she learned to listen. It came to her gradually that she was experiencing something that gave her a prophetic vision, an insight into suffering, and the certainty of the slow, faithful working of God. She lived it day by day in her own being, in her own griefs and growing understanding, her isolation and widowhood, the consolation that had come to her. Slowly the words began to grow within her, not to be spoken, but ready: 'Yet there is hope.'

She waited, and the years moved by in seasons of sowing and reaping, birth and death, and many that she knew and loved died, and she was left. Then, one day, news came for her from Jerusalem. The youngest of the family sent word to tell her that her mother, Miriam, had died and to invite her to come and live with them: to be a grandmother to the children, to receive from them the hospitality and care that thirty years ago she had given them. It was not easy to say farewell to the village that was her home, or to Ezra's children, or to the life of chosen solitude that had formed around her, but she sensed profoundly that this was the moment of change from which all else would flow.

They gave her a small room of her own, a welcome to their meals, a share in their family life and she was content. The bustling vigour of Jerusalem was all around her; the stillness of her own soul was within. And the prophetic word grew in her, giving her that sense of delight of a cherished secret. As years passed, she began to speak: the new Temple of Herod rose up, gleaming in marble and gold, ornate and magnificent, but she saw beyond its grandeur to something else, far simpler, far more beautiful. 'There is hope,' she said, to those who were ready to hear. 'Not this Temple built to placate us, to hold us in thrall with its walls and courtyards. Hope of a new dawn of mercy, a promise of restoration that cannot be contained within these walls or represented by its dazzling hard whiteness of facade.' Some gathered round to hear her as she stood at the entrance of the Court of Women. Simeon, almost as old as herself. Others, whose patient, faithful lives were, like hers, on the edge. Whose faces showed the years' engraving of sorrows.

Now each day was focused on the careful preparation of her place of waiting in the outer court of the Temple. She rarely left, taking only those steps that were necessary to meet her needs. She remembered the promise given to her tribe, long ago. 'Your strength will match your days.' She knew that long life was given to her in order to see the beginning of a new order. That was her calling. All of her years were gathering now to a day that was coming. Sometimes she looked back in memory to see the long journey that lay behind her. Not a journey of distance, though it had been a harsh path of miles walked alone, years ago. It was hard, from this place of hope and clear light, to remember the anguish of darkened places. The pain had dulled, perhaps, but she did not think it was simply the passing of time. It was as if the pain of widowhood, the terrors of isolation and helplessness, had sharpened something within, had given her clearer sight, had burnished her soul to transparency year after year, until she could stand now, waiting, certain, her senses stretching out, her face turned eagerly to look far beyond the city walls to the great canopy of the skies. She began to understand that the holiest places, the places where she, a woman, could never enter, were not the places where God made his home, his resting place. These courts, these rituals of sacrifice, festival and duty, were not the path that drew human beings closer to God. They set limits, excluded, even mocked, the poor, the desperate, the widowed and crippled, who came with empty hands.

She waited patiently for what she knew was the coming of the Eternal, the mystery of the ages, the hope of her people and of all people. Her own great age shrank to nothing in the face of eternity. And then, one day, they came. A young mother, a careful husband carrying the two doves required for sacrifice, and a little child, a baby of a few weeks. Simeon, standing watching, like herself, stepped forward transfigured, his cloudy eyes raised heavenward with joy. 'I can go in peace,' he said. 'I have seen the salvation of the world.'

Anna stepped forward also to take the child and speak over him the delight of all her longings, the love and joy that took away, no, she realised, made an offering of, her barren griefs and widowhood, her waiting and longing. And the baby gazed at her, resting in her arms for one long age of consolation before she spoke, crying out her prophetic wonder. Around her the people gathered, and wondered, and were silent in the awe of what they had seen and heard. 'Who is this? Where are they from? Who is this child?' The questions flowed like the rustling of leaves. She knew she had held within her trembling and withered arms, the One for whom creation longed, the One whose place had been prepared on the golden throne of the Ark, the mercy seat of God. He had come, and she had gazed into his eyes, and seen the movement of his hands.

She spoke few words except to say, 'I have seen him. He has come to us. The hope of Israel, the promise of God.' The wonder of it lingered among the crowds, but the agitation of the city, buying and selling, news and conflict, birth and death, rose up to smother the miracle of a morning's light. She accepted that, because she was certain that there would be a time, some thirty years or so hence, when this child would stride forward as a grown man to speak to his people.

Simeon was found rigid in the sleep of death one evening, his face still turned upward to the sky. She wept for him as for the loss of a brother, but did not mourn his death, knowing his joy was fulfilled.

Her own life faded now. She knew the ancient promise of strength that had sustained her for all her eighty-four years. It will not be long now, she told herself. But soon, even as she withdrew to seek solitude again, Jerusalem hummed once more with news, rumours, wild speculation. A group of travellers from the East, wise men and wealthy, some said, agog with the strangeness of it. Travellers from the East, visiting the palace of King Herod. And then, handed down in whispers, from steward to servant to slave, the news of their errand. The search for a child, born King of the Jews. Ancient prophecies were brought out by the religious leaders to show that he was to be born in Bethlehem, the town of David's birth. Herod's cruelty, his ruthlessness would not make way for a rival. All Jerusalem knew that: and drew breath, waiting for the steps he would take to find and destroy. Even destroy these travellers, no matter how wealthy or powerful they might be in their own country. And then the story of his craftiness, his cleverness, was muttered in the courts of the palace until it became the gossip of the wine shops and the market. 'Go to Bethlehem and find him, and tell me how I can come and pay him homage.' The mocking, silent laughter hung behind his seemingly reverent words.

Two days passed and the three travellers did not return. On the third day, towards evening, Anna was driven by some strange urgency to leave the Temple, to leave the streets of her home and the shelter of all that was familiar to her. She now stood watching by the gate that led south from the palace, turning her face towards Bethlehem, stretching her soul in prayer for that small family. She saw suddenly a detachment of the palace guard spurring out onto the road south. 'Out of the way, old woman,' cried one, thrusting her against the stone of the city gate, so that she struck her head and fell. The last of the horse's hooves skidded by her body and thudded away in the churning dust. Even in those moments of pain and terror, she knew with certainty that all would be well with the family. Just as she also knew that the cost to others of this king's brutality was somehow held in the timeless consolation she had seen in the eyes of the child. Her small body, frail now and weary with years, was glad to fall into that keeping.

Her eyes caught a last glimpse of the soldiers riding away amidst a cloud of reddening dust in the evening light. Despite her weakness, despite her knowledge of their terrible errand, she was suddenly laughing, laughing with the knowledge that the child she had held was now holding her. And that she had entered into the innermost courts of his true Temple.

Reflection

Anna, of the Tribe of Asher, has two verses in Luke's Gospel (Luke 2:36–38), but those verses are full of content, full of potential story. She would have endured the horror of war and occupation and its turbulence before the occupation secured a sort of stability. She was a widow and very old and there's no indication of children. So, like so many of the women in our story, she would have been marginalised and poor.

- *I have given her a story of grief and bitterness and then turned the story into something else. What do you think are the turning points for her – the experiences that become redemptive?*

- *As a woman, she is excluded from the inner courts of the Temple. Yet God comes to her and turns the Temple inside out. Are women still being excluded in the church?*

- *She is a prophet. What is a prophet, and what could their role be now, in our society? Does the church have a prophetic role? If so, what issues should/must we engage with?*

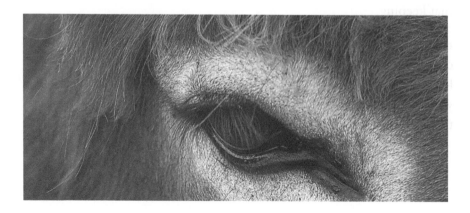

HINDSIGHT

Well, of course, Sir, if I'd known, I'd never have done it. Not if I'd known it mattered to his Royal Greatness, or to you, Sir.

(Wine for the Captain, girl, and quick about it.)

Here, Sir, unbuckle a bit, as you might say, and take the weight off your feet. Here in the shade. It's a long ride in the heat of the day. Your men too. Marching, you say? Well, they can sit over there, and I'll get the girl to serve them just as soon as she brings you a cup of our best.

(Here, Susanna, open a cask of rough for the men and some bread and cheese for all. Look sharp.)

As I say, I'd never have done it. Not if I'd known. But you know how it is, Sir! We was rushed off our feet with visitors from all over, wanting a bed, wanting a meal, a room, wine, stabling, fodder, and the town packed with the crush. Not a room in the place, nor anywhere else in the town, neither.

But can I offer you food, Sir, before you and your men take to the road again? We have a lamb, freshly killed yesterday, with bread and wine? No?

That young couple, you say?

They was nothing special. A young man, decent enough, and his girl, nearly due by the look of her. Tired out both of them and arriving just as we were shutting up for the night. Mind you, they wasn't from round here. Strangers. Northerners. Know what I mean? They didn't belong. Well what could I do? If I'd known I might've found a room somewhere, but I didn't know, and that's a fact. So I put them in the outhouse, well, more of a shed really where the horses are stabled and the goats go in the winter and they was thankful enough for that. A roof over them and straw for bedding. One of the servant girls, our Rachel, went to help when she'd done her chores, but I couldn't let her go until after midnight. My wife took them a couple of blankets and bread and wine. And hot water, later. When the baby came.

Odd that. Are you a father yourself, Sir? … Not that you know of! Well, we won't go there. Plenty of time when you want to settle down. But it's odd how it gets you. I remember my first. First watch of the night and that thin little cry and the whole earth stops for a moment. And you think, my God! It's real! And we'd just done washing up the crocks and sweeping up and the night was as silent as the tomb, and that same thin cry. That's when my wife went with rags and water to help the girl.

Nothing in it really. Strangers. Young couple, new baby. Far from home. But the next thing we have a stumbling bunch of shepherds down from the hills, bursting with some craziness about light and angels and songs of glory. I had to tell them to keep their voices down and not disturb my guests as they traipsed down the street, but they'd come to see him. The baby, and that girl and her husband! All crowding into that shed, falling over their clumsy feet as they tried to tiptoe in and stinking of sheep shit and ewe grease, begging your pardon. Falling over themselves to see a baby! We didn't get rid of them till dawn.

Where did they go next? The family? Well, I was glad to see the back of them. More than enough trouble for one night. They stayed – we did find them a room after a couple of days – until the girl was strong enough to move after her seven days and then they got lodgings in the town. I didn't see them again. No. Though when I heard who'd next come to visit them, I wish they'd stayed with me, I can tell you. Three foreigners, wealthy enough to pay for my best rooms and the jars of Samos wine I keep hidden in the cellar. They would have set me up. But I never saw them. I only heard that they came at night, camels and mules plodding down our streets with no one to guide them to the house and then they were off before daybreak. I missed my chance there.

The family? you say. Where are they staying? Well, I don't rightly know. My wife might know, but she's at the end of the town, visiting our eldest. She's got a two-year-old already and another on the way. She'll come back with all the news but you can't wait, you say? What's that? Boy or girl? My grandchild? It's a girl. No sons in our family, nor grandsons neither, more's the pity. Yes, a girl. They lead you a dance, then cost you a dowry.

You must get moving? Well, Captain, Sir, I hope you've been comfortable with us, you and your men, and found all to your satisfaction. Remember us, if you will. A word from the Captain of the Royal Regiment would be a real favour. But as I say, if I had known, I'd have taken more trouble, given them the best in the house, you might say. And kept in touch.

Anything his Majesty commands – and you too, Sir.

It's been an honour to look after you, Sir, you and your men. Keep the change? Well, thank you, Sir. For my granddaughter's dowry? Well, that's very kind of you. I'll tell my daughter to keep it safe for her. We'll remember you, Captain, and if we can serve you again, we'll be proud to do so.

Reflection

Just five words, 'no room at the inn' (Luke 2:7), gave me the idea for this story. I've imagined the innkeeper and how he was caught up in the immediate events. He's just an ordinary man, stressed and busy and with the kind of reactions we all might have under pressure. Asked for information, he's eager to ingratiate himself and keep on the right side of the Captain of the king's guard.

- *Are there any situations that you've faced in life that have challenged you like this?*
- *What situations in the world today most resemble this story? How can we pray? What else can we do?*

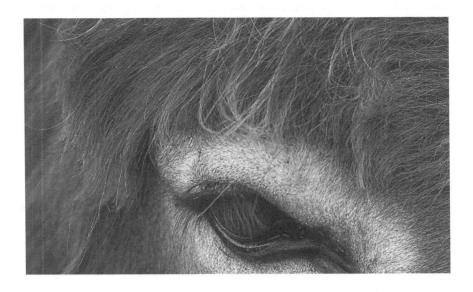

GIFTS

We met in a hall of stars.
Talking, night after night,
Pointing, plucking at sleeves, parchments, charts.
Gestures of old men
Who sense at last their studious devotion might
Lead beyond themselves.
And in the night sky, the star waited, consuming us.

Our gifts were chosen lightly, easily decided,
Certain of our quest, impatient
To pursue a lifetime's vision.

Gold, we said. Kingship, wealth,
Essence of all treasure of earth and heaven.
Purity, poured richly from the crucible,
Formed of fire itself.
Incense of priesthood. That too
Easily chosen. Precious, prayerful,
Drifting in clouds of fragrant longing
Between man and God.
King and priest. We knew that.
The star spoke of it, sang the words
To us in the throbbing darkness as we travelled.
But myrrh? We brought it wondering, troubled.
Not understanding the compulsion
That sealed those precious vials in their casket.

So, we journeyed, and in the early days
Excitement like youth compelled us.
At night we scoured the skies
Tracing the great procession of the stars
And our star, his star, moving westward
Urging us forward.

As days, weeks, passed,
So these treasures in our arms
Gathered into a great heaviness.
Now, each felt the heft of choice
And those deliberations, abstract, reasoned,
Fled from memory, and meaning fled and left
Only substance, leaden in our caskets.
Inert and futile.

Gold: the weariness of government.
Imperial power: despot, tyrant,
Crazed with its compulsion, while
Usurpers lodged secretly within corners of the mind.
And the lure of wealth
And its devouring lust.

Frankincense, clouded
With the unnumbered prayers
And longings of humanity. Our guilt
And failings. The yearning of devotion.
The barren mystery of unanswered prayer.

It grew too dense
To carry in my arms, beneath my cloak,
And so I bore it on my saddle-bow
And so my poor beast stumbled
Under its weight.

Myrrh, in its consecrated chest,
Was carried last among us,
With swaying tiredness. The helplessness
And dread of our mortality,
Mourning and pain and loss.
Our fragile longing also
That the embalmed body
Might somehow carry the spirit beyond death.

Strange gifts to bring to a child. A baby
Whose wondering hands touched
And received them.

We gave him all
Our hapless heaviness,
Returning lightened, on a road, a journey,
Altogether different.

Reflection

We travel towards Bethlehem again with the Wise Men and explore the meaning of their gifts, before we turn so soon to Lent and Easter.

In this poem, I've tried to travel with them as the weight of their gifts becomes heavier and heavier, as they think about their symbolic meaning.

Then, they come at last to the Child, and are released as he receives them.

'Come to me, all who are weary and heavy-burdened, and I will give you rest' (Matthew 11:28–30, NRSV).

Let us, at the end of this journey, give him 'all our hapless heaviness' and go on our way, lightened. Amen

ACKNOWLEDGEMENTS

Some of these pieces were first published in *Recognition*, by Janet Killeen, 2019, Kindle and paperback available on Amazon

'When the time had fully come' printed by kind permission of the editors of *Merry Christmas Everyone,* published by the Association of Christian Writers, 2018

Passages from NRSV copyright 1989, Division of Christian Education of the National Council of the Churches of Christ in the United States of America. Used by permission. All rights reserved.